HUNTER'S MOON
for Horn and Orchestra

GILBERT VINTER

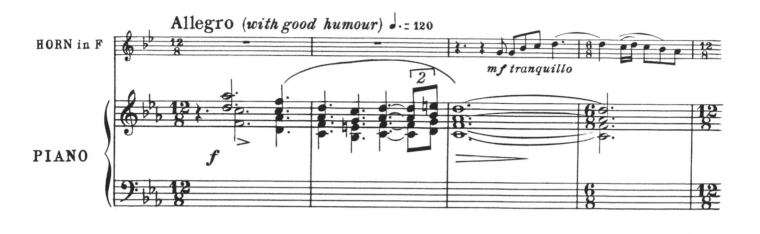

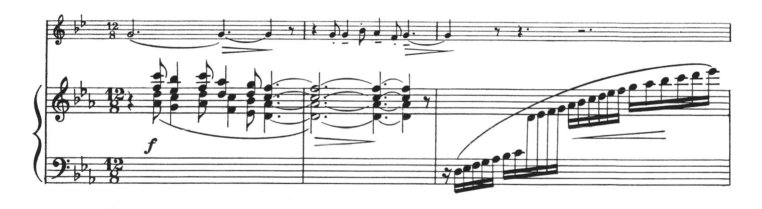

2

Hunter's Moon

Hunter's Moon

H. 15506

4

(sost.)

Hunter's Moon

Gaily

6

Hunter's Moon

Horn in F

H. 15506

Reproduced and printed by
Halstan & Co. Ltd., Amersham, Bucks., England

Horn in F

HUNTER'S MOON

GILBERT VINTER

Horn in F

H. 15508

Gilbert Vinter

HUNTER'S MOON

for
Horn and Orchestra

Reduction for
Horn and Piano

Boosey & Hawkes Music Publishers Ltd
www.boosey.com

Lento (*very tenderly*)

Hunter's Moon

H. 15506

8

Hunter's Moon

Hunter's Moon

H. 15506

Tempo I

Giocoso

Hunter's Moon

Hunter's Moon

H. 15506

Reproduced and printed by
Halstan & Co. Ltd., Amersham, Bucks., England